My sister is different

Written and illustrated by
Sarah Tamsin Hunter

Let me try to explain...

Sometimes we have play fights but my sister doesn't understand…

and she punches me too hard.

This is because she can't understand how I feel. (Even if I explain to her how I feel sometimes.)

Our fence is high.

We use a security lock to keep my sister in.

4

This is what would happen to my sister, if the fence were too low.

This is because she doesn't understand that cars might hurt her.

Once when we were walking in the town my sister started crying in the newsagents and she started throwing magazines about.

Dad decided to get us some ice cream to help her feel better and to cheer us up. I ate all my ice cream. I gave some to my sister but she threw it away and the seagulls ate it.

She got as mad as a bull. My sister was crying for three hours! She gave me a BIG headache! As big as a mountain.

My sister goes on lots of trips
with her school.

Special helpers go
with them and
hold their hands in
case they wander
off or need help.

At my school it is different.
We mainly work at our
lessons in school.

Sometimes we go
on trips, like to an
art gallery, where
we know to stay
in a group.

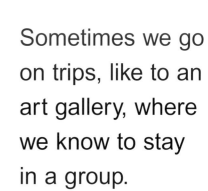

Once we went out for tea and my
sister sprinkled salt on her ice cream!

People stared.

She doesn't understand the difference between salt and sugar. She went to the toilet because she felt sick.

11

Once we went to Edinburgh Zoo.

Even though my sister is quite big now, it is safer and more comfortable for her to be in her special pushchair.

I help Katie to learn to say new words.

She likes it when I do this with her.

13

I don't like it when my sister starts colouring the pictures I have drawn.

14

I scrunch up my pictures when they are coloured by my sister.

She giggles when I throw the coloured pictures into the bin.

She doesn't understand that the pictures I draw are important to me.

15

My sister always fiddles with the TV controls.

She ignores me
when I talk to her.

This is because
when she is busy
she doesn't hear
anything else.

At bedtime, my sister wakes up crying.
This ruins my bedtime.

She might have a nightmare or feel cold.

My parents take her through to their bed and she feels safe.

I love my sister.